Don't Squash
FLUFFY!

Also by
Gabriel Fitzmaurice

**Published by Poolbeg Press
(all for children)**

Don't Squash FLUFFY!

Gabriel Fitzmaurice

POEMS FOR CHILDREN AND THEIR PARENTS

Illustrations by
Steven Hope

POOLBEG
FOR CHILDREN

Published 2004
Poolbeg Press Ltd.
123 Grange Hill, Baldoyle,
Dublin 13, Ireland
Email: poolbeg@poolbeg.com

1 3 5 7 9 10 8 6 4 2

A catalogue record for this book is available from the British Library.

ISBN 1-84223-159-6

Illustrations by Steven Hope
Typeset by Patricia Hope in Stone Serif 10.5/14

Printed by
Cox & Wyman
Reading, Berkshire

www.poolbeg.com

Biography

Gabriel Fitzmaurice was born in 1952, in the village of Moyvane, Co. Kerry where he still lives. He has been teaching in the local national school, where he is now principal teacher, since 1975. He is the author of more than thirty books, including collections of poetry in English and Irish as well as several collections of verse for children. He has translated extensively from the Irish and has edited a number of anthologies of poetry in Irish and English. He has published a volume of essays, Kerry on my Mind, and collections of songs and ballads. A cassette of his poems, The Space Between: New and Selected Poems 1984-1992 is also available. He frequently broadcasts on radio and television on education and the arts.

For John and Nessa,
without whom . . .

Contents

Imagination

Imagination is the thing that
Makes you magic
And
Gives you
Inspiration to make everything
New,
And
To
Invent things that are
Only seen by you, where
Nothing is impossible. Imagine!

Dogs' Tails in the Morning

The dogs' tails went like wipers
When I let them out today;
The dogs' tails went like wipers
Wiping gloom away;

The dogs' tails went like wipers
As they jumped about with joy
Happy just to be alive.
And so was I!

Pooh

Does pooh always come from your bottom?
Mammy I *need* to find out.
I hope it just comes from your bottom.
I'd hate if it came from my mouth.

My Auntie for Stella

I call my uncles "uncle",
But no! I simply can't
No matter how I try to
Call Annette my "aunt"
'Cos she's my *auntie.*

"Aunt" is for a person
You're not too sure about,
The kind, when she comes to visit,
Makes you feel you should keep out

And let her talk to Mammy,
But an auntie's not like that –
She's the kind that hugs you
And you want to hug her back.

Yes! Annette's my *auntie,*
The one that joins in play,
And Mammy has just told me
She's coming here to stay.
MY AUNTIE!

Checkin' my Wellies for Spiders

I'm checkin' my wellies for spiders,
I turn them upside-down;
I'm checkin' my wellies for spiders
Before I put them on.

I'm checkin' my wellies for spiders
'Cos they might be inside –
I know if I was a spider
'Twould be a brilliant hide.

I'm checkin' my wellies for spiders,
Once I had no fear
Of creepy things like spiders,
But now I just can't bear

The thought of touching crawlies –
They give me the creeps
So I'm checkin' my wellies for spiders
Before I put in my feet.
Yeah! I'm checkin' my wellies for spiders
Before I put in my feet.

I'd Like To Be a Wrestler

I'd like to be a wrestler
With tree trunks for my thighs,
My hands as big as shovels,
Volcanoes for my eyes.

And if I was a wrestler
I'd be The JCB
For that's what they'd all call me.
Oh my! the things you'd see –

You'd see me lifting wrestlers
And throwing them around
And sitting down upon them
When I had them on the ground;

I'd jump on them and throw them
Out of the wrestling ring,
And when I am the champion
(Just think of it!) I'll bring

My belt back home to Mammy
And she'll be proud of me
And then she'll know her little girl
Has become The JCB.
That's me!

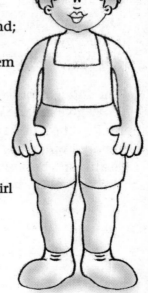

"Daddy, Will You Answer Me?"

"Daddy, will you answer me?
You're only saying 'um',
Are you saying *yes* or *no?*;
Daddy, are you dumb?"

"Dad, I could talk to you like that
But I'm more fizzilized;
Daddy, will you answer me
In words I reckinize?"

"Daddy, will you answer me?
Dad, I'm not your friend.
OK, Dad, I'm going to sleep.
Goodbye. Goodnight. THE END."

I Can Make my Daddy Smile

I can make my daddy smile
When he's mad at me,
I can make my daddy smile
Though he's mad as mad can be –

I just purr "Who's a moody boy?"
And maybe pull his nose
And a smile starts up behind his eyes
And grows and grows and grows

Till Dad can hide his smile no more
And I watch it spread
Till the smile that Daddy tried to stop
Is all around his head.
Yes, the smile that Daddy tried to stop
Is all around his head!

Hallowe'en Brack

I cut a slice for Mammy
And I cut a slice for Dad
And I cut two slices for myself
But it wasn't to be had,

The ring that I was hoping for.
I cut and cut and cut
And gave Mam and Dad more slices.
I'd almost given up –

I thought I'd have to cut it all
And eat it every bit
When I struck a wrapper with my knife
And when I opened it
It was the ring! I put it on!

It was a perfect fit!

Daddy is a Mop-Top

He grew up in the 'sixties
With Beatles' mop-top hair
And still his hair is mop-top;
But Daddy doesn't care

That it's the height of fashion
To shave your head today,
Daddy is a mop-top
And that's the way he'll stay

No matter that his bald patch
Is spreading, and his hair
Is greying 'round his temples,
Daddy doesn't care

'Cos Daddy is a mop-top,
His hair goes its own way –
He's stuck back in the 'sixties
And that's the way he'll stay.
He's stuck back in the 'sixties
And that's the way he'll stay.

Yeah! Yeah! Yeah!

Spreading Slurry

Close the windows! Quick! Quick! Quick!
Close the doors or you'll be sick.
They're spreading slurry, oh the stink!
The smell's so bad you can hardly think.
And the smell gets up your nose,
In your hair and on your clothes,
But the farmer doesn't mind one bit,
He says there's money where there's . . .
Slurry!

Pidgin

Most teachers talk pidgin
In a way you'd never dream
Of talking to your neighbours.
It's enough to make you scream!

"Get the *bosca bruascair*,"
"Eat your *lón* at *sos*,"
"Close your *mála scoile*,"
"*Ag siúl* out to the bus."

I know they're trying to teach us
But it's pidgin just the same
(And they call me "Pádraig"
Though Paddy is my name).

School does that to teachers –
They mix up all their words;
They're only trying to teach us
But it sounds absurd.

I know they're trying to teach us
But still it sounds absurd.

Virginia Lawler Won't Hold my Hand

Virginia Lawler won't hold my hand
And I'm very sad;
We were playing buses
Out here in the yard

And Virginia Lawler held my hand
And we were playing away,
Now Virginia Lawler won't hold my hand
'Cos she don't want to play.

Virginia Lawler won't be my friend
And I just don't know why
And it's no use trying to cheer me up,
I think I'm going to cry
But here comes Jenny playing trains –
I love playing trains!
Bye-bye.

Duty for Niamh Culhane

"Please, teacher! Please, teacher! Please, teacher!
Who is the beauty today?"
The teacher looks down at the Infant.
Who's the beauty? Just what can she say?
So she asks what she means by "the beauty"
And this is all Niamh can say:
"You know, miss, the beauty, the *beauty* –
The teacher who minds us at play."

*Duty: i.e. yard duty, minding
the children in the yard at
playtime*

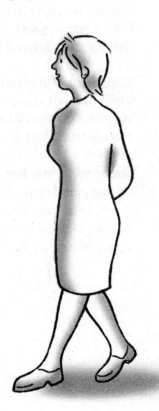

Can I Bring my Hamster to School, Dad?

Can I bring my hamster to school, Dad?
Please can I bring him today?
Can I bring my hamster to school, Dad?
Please, Dad, what do you say?

Can I bring my hamster to school, Dad?
Jimmy brought his yesterday.
Can I bring my hamster to school, Dad?
Please can I bring him today?

Can I bring my hamster to school, Dad?
He'll love all the girls and boys
And the girls and boys will all love him,
He's better to play with than toys.

Can I bring my hamster to school, Dad?
Please can I bring him today?
Can I bring my hamster to school, Dad?
Please, Dad, what do you say?
Can I bring my hamster to school?

My Tooth Fell into your Bag

My tooth fell into your bag,
My tooth fell into your bag,
I wanted to mind it,
But now I can't find it
'Cos my tooth fell into your bag.

My tooth fell into your bag,
My tooth fell into your bag,
It was such a beaut,
A pearl of a tooth
But my tooth fell into your bag.

My tooth fell into your bag,
My tooth fell into your bag,
I've searched through the books,
I've looked and I've looked
For my tooth that fell into your bag.

My tooth fell into your bag,
My tooth fell into your bag
And my prospects are glum,
Now the fairy won't come
'Cos my tooth fell into your bag.

Splat!

It didn't come from outer space
(If it did, I wouldn't care) –
Oh no! it was much worse than that
When a bird pooped on my hair.

I was minding my own business
Playing in the yard
When I felt this *plop* upon my head
Catching me off guard.

When I reached up to investigate,
I felt this sticky goo,
And all my friends were laughing
That my hair was stuck with pooh;

And then I started crying –
I cried most bitterly
That of all the places that pooh could land
It had to land on me.

And I wouldn't let them wash me –
Oh Lord! it wasn't fair
So I just sat and sulked and sobbed
That a bird pooped on my hair.
I just sat and sulked and sobbed
That a bird pooped on my hair.

N Is for What Animal

We played this game in class today
(It was the teacher's game),
We had to go through the alphabet
To let the letters name

Animals or bugs or birds,
The letters gave a clue –
A for Ant, B for Bear,
C for Cockatoo . . .

We were going through the alphabet
And when it was my turn
I turned red as Man. United,
My face began to burn

For my animal began with N
(Is there such a one at all?
That's what I was thinking)
When I heard Patricia call:

"Please, sir! Please, sir! I know it!"
Which made me turn more red –
Until I heard her animal
("A Noctapus," she said)
And when we'd finished laughing
'Twas her face that was red

Tōtō Spaghetti

I thought I knew my football,
I know lots of stuff
But no matter how much you think you know
It never is enough.

Like the time the teacher mentioned
That the Man. United team
Were buying Toto Spaghetti;
I thought I'd heard of him

So I said I knew about it,
That he played for Real Madrid
(Although I wasn't certain
At least I thought he did),

And when the whole class laughed at me
I knew he'd called my bluff,
Oh! no matter how much you think you know
It never is enough.
No matter how much you think you know
It never is enough.

The Mime

I had to make a mime
(How easy can it get?)
Of waking up one morning,
Going out to feed my pet

And finding that my pet had died;
I mimed my great distress
(I could tell no-one about it –
My classmates had to guess).

Tom said I was sleepy,
And then to my surprise
John thought I was miming
That dust got in my eyes;

Some said I was exhausted
Or bored with the TV;
More said I was thinking,
And goodness gracious me!

Betty said "I have it!
There's onions in your eyes
Cos anyone who chops them
Cries";

Joe thought I had a nightmare,
Paddy said 'twas sweat
And all the while I'm thinking
How easy can it get;
But no-one in my class today
Guessed about my pet.

Taking Thought

Sometimes if you know too much
You take the wrong approach –
I answered wrong in the quiz today
When asked what was a roach.

My brain was thinking "cockroach" –
"An insect," I replied;
The teacher said 'twas a kind of fish
And I could not see why.

And later on the teacher
Asked me "What's a perch?"
And again my thinking let me down –
When my mind went into SEARCH

I saw every bird I ever knew
Perched upon its tree,
So I answered "It's a bird"
But the teacher said to me

"It's not your day at all, my man.
It's a fish," I heard him say.
Sometimes my mind's no help at all
When thought leads me astray.

Sometimes my mind's no help at all
When thought leads me astray.

At the Zoo

Last year on our school tour
We all went to the zoo,
We spent the whole day up there,
There was lots of things to do.

We saw camels there and crocodiles
And snakes and parrots too,
And bears, a hippopotamus
And a baby kangaroo.

We went into the monkey house –
We went in there with glee
'Cos we all love the monkeys
(They're great fun, you see);

I went over to the monkey cage
To have a closer look
When a monkey piddled in my eye –
Oh boy! what rotten luck.

The monkey just came over
And piddled in my eye
And I had nothing but my sleeve
To wipe it dry

And I cursed that cheeky monkey
And I cursed the silly Zoo
But my friends all started laughing
And I started laughing too
(What else could I do?)

Yes! I started laughing with them,
But until the day I die
I won't forget the monkey
That piddled in my eye,
No! I won't forget the monkey
That piddled in my eye.

Cookery Class

Now boys and girls, this morning
We're making scrambled egg.
Children, are you listening?
Stop your fooling, Greg!
Jenny, pay attention –
Put away that book!
Today we're making scrambled egg.
Are you ready, children? Look!
The most important thing you have to learn
Look up here I say!
Is how to break the eggshell.
This is the proper way.
Children, are you looking?
It's most important! I'll
Show you how to break an egg
And then I'll let you try.
Everybody looking!
(This sure is a bore!)
But, as she goes to break it,
The egg slips on the floor!
It slips out of her fingers
And breaks about her legs.
(That'll teach her to go on about
How to break an egg!)

When Sally Got Sick in the Bus

We went to this play in the theatre
All about kids just like us,
'Twas twenty-four miles back to Newtown
And Sally got sick in the bus.

She hadn't been eating or drinking
Stuff that she shouldn't. No way!
She just sat in her seat and was telling
Her friends what she liked in the play;

And when we got back to the village,
The teacher stood up in the bus
And told us to gather our rubbish
And walk into school without fuss
When Sally turned pale as a candle
And puked up her guts in the bus.

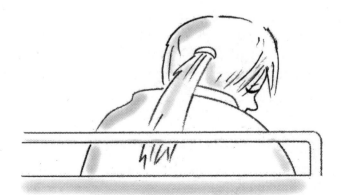

She just sat and she puked without warning
She'd no time to tell us watch out
But we knew someone puked when we smelled it
And we dashed to the door to get out.

We got out double quick I can tell you,
Glad to be shut of the pong
With never a thought for the driver
Who'd smell it as he drove along.

We got out double quick I can tell you
With hustle and bustle and fuss
Holding our noses and coughing
When Sally got sick in the bus,
Glad to be shut of the puke-stink
When Sally got sick in the bus.

Raffle

We had a raffle in our class
For stickers for a play
And I was hoping that I'd win
So I began to pray

That I'd win a sticker,
I prayed and prayed each time
The teacher pulled a name out
But the name was never mine.

I prayed and prayed that I would win
But no matter how I tried
My name just stayed inside the box –
Oh Lord! I nearly cried.

But still I learned that though you pray,
The raffle's still the same,
It just goes on and on and on
And the ticket with your name

Stays inside the raffle box
Until your luck is in
And today was not my day
And so I didn't win.

No! today was not my day
And so I didn't win.

Pups

The teacher was giving out
To the boys for being cross –
He said he'd never seen so many
Pups in the one class.

I don't know why I did it
But I wrote "pups are cute"
In my homework copy –
But the teacher saw me do it.

He called me up to face the class
And said before them all,
"Please explain why pups are cute."
"They bang into the wall,"

I said,
"And seem never to get bruised."
He only told me to sit down.
(I think he was amused!)

The First of September

The kids are going back to the "National"
But I don't go there any more –
I spent eight years in the "National"
(Been there since I was just four).

So I stand by the wall looking at them
As they troop in in ones, twos and threes
And they glance at my newly found freedom –
I bet they all wish they were me!

And I talk to my friends there assembled
Across the divide of that wall
But I find that my friends in the schoolyard
Don't mind being back there at all.

And though I've moved on from the "National",
I just had to come here today
To see all my friends and my neighbours
With whom I will never more play

In the yard at each break in the "National",
Those friends I have played with for years;
Though I came here to show off my freedom,
Now I am closer to tears.

For I'm leaving the school in the village
Where I spent oh! *such* happy days;
Goodbye to the school in the village,
Now is the parting of ways.

And tomorrow in the big Comprehensive
I must start a new life on my own,
And though I'm excited about it
And everyone says how I've grown,

Here today in the "National"
Though I came to show off at the wall,
I found that what I intended
Is not how it turned out at all.
Oh! often the way we intend things
Is not how it turns out at all.

Peeling the Goose

There's a picture in my book
Of a woman with a bird,
She's pulling off the feathers;
I didn't know the word –

It looked like she was peeling
So I said she peeled the goose
And my friends all started laughing
And calling *me* a goose.

Ah yes! They started laughing
'Cos I didn't know the word,
But my word for it was better
'Cos it makes you see the bird

In a way that "plucking" doesn't
'Cos anyone can use
A common word like "plucking"
About any common goose

But when I said she *peeled* it,
'Twas *peeling* that you saw –
Like you'd peel an orange,
A common goose no more.

Oh, when I said she *peeled* it,
You saw the goose anew
Because I used a different word.
That's what words can do.

He Sings When He's on the Toilet

He sings when he's on the toilet
(He talks to himself as well),
He thinks there's no one listening
And we all have to quell

Our giggles at his antics
While he's sitting on the throne
(Somehow, when you're in there
You think you're all alone

And so you start up singing
And making speeches too
'Cos you think no one can hear you
When you're sitting on the loo.
Oh, you think no one can hear you
When you're sitting on the loo).
But they can!

Self-Portrait

We had to make a self-portrait
(Imagine! A picture of me!)
And put positive things in about us
But what could I write about me?

'Twas no trouble drawing the picture
But I couldn't put in (though I tried)
Five positive things that described me:
I felt bunched up and threatened inside.

And the teacher came over and asked me
What was the matter. So I
Said I was stuck and I couldn't
Think of positive things I could write.

He just smiled and we had a discussion
About things that I like in my friends
And he wrote down the list on the blackboard
('Twas so long that you'd think 'twouldn't end).

And we looked at the list and we chatted
And he asked me what did I see
And I realized then what I like in my friends
Are the things that I like about me.

So I wrote down my list from the blackboard
Glowing and glad that I could
Write positive things on my portrait.
Some days in school, man!, are good.

The Boy who Talks Back to the Television

He talks back to the television,
He just can't help it. So
He talks back to the television
And makes a holy show

Of himself when watching
Even the teatime news;
He talks back to the television
Bursting to air his views.

He talks back to the television
When he's watching games
Like snooker, tennis, football
And calls the players names –

You'd think that they could hear him
But he doesn't mind
(He knows that they can't hear him
But talks back all the time)

'Cos it doesn't matter
That it can't hear his squawk,
He'll have his say, he'll have his way
Even if he has to talk

Back to the television,
He'll have his say, don't fear,
'Cos even if no-one's listening,
Someone's bound to hear.

Even if no-one's listening,
Someone's bound to hear.

The Showman

You say that I'm a showman
Because I like to do
Things you shy away from –
Like telling this to you.

Where I'd give information,
You close up like a clam –
Go on, call me a showman
Though that's not all I am.

Go on then, keep your secrets,
Hide everything that's true
Because you think that hiding
Is the safest thing to do.

Go on, call me a showman,
It shows that you're afraid
Of what they'd think about you,
Of what might be said

If, once, you told your story,
Hid nothing, told it true,
So instead you call me showman –
The easy thing to do.
Go on, call me a showman
While I tell the truth for you.

Freedom

Everyone expects me
To do what's expected of me,
And I've always done what's expected
'Cos I do what's expected, you see.

Oh, I always do what's expected
(You keep out of trouble that way,
But people just take you for granted –
They expect you to do what they say).

But no more will I do what's expected,
I'll speak up for myself come what may
And I won't be taken for granted
'Cos people will watch what they say

When they know I won't do what's expected
Just because it's expected of me,
I'll do what is right though I have to fight
If that is the price of being free.
Yes! I'll do what is right though I have to fight
If that is the price of being free.

Clouds

Clouds are amazing –
They're more than all you know
That school books say about them.
Oh my, the things they show!

They're moving pictures in the sky
Changing as you look,
And anyone who explains a cloud
From a book

Isn't looking at a cloud –
It's more than books can show:
Books can tell you what it is,
Explain a cloud, but no!
You've got to be a cloud yourself
To really, really know.

You've got to be a cloud yourself
To really, really know.

My Tick-Tock Clock

With a tick-tock clock
I can sleep at night,
With a tick-tock clock
Everything's all right
'Cos a tick-tock clock
Beside your bed
Is the sound of safe
Inside your head.
Tick-tock, tick-tock, tick-tock.
Goodnight!

What Is the Stars?

Where is the man in Orion?
Where is the plough in the Plough?
Where is the dog in the Dog Star?
I don't see, Daddy, just how

You can see all those things just by looking,
To me they're just stars in the sky;
How did they think of those names, Dad,
And why did they name those stars? Why?

I can see many things in the clouds, Dad,
They make pictures up there in the sky,
Things I can see or imagine,
But I can't though I try and I try

See the man in the stars of Orion
Or the plough in the stars of the Plough
Or the dog in the star of the Dog Star.
I can't see them, Daddy – nohow!

Leemie 'Lone

Leemie 'Lone is lazy,
All he does is moan.
When you ask him to do anything,
He whimpers, "Leemie 'lone."

"Leemie 'lone," he whimpers
Loafing on the couch,
A slob, a couch potato,
A lazy-bones, a slouch.

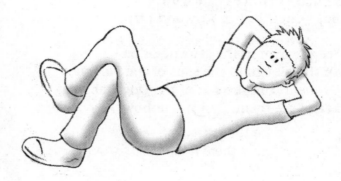

"Leemie 'lone," he whimpers –
All he wants is to be left alone
Watching television
In the *DON'T DISTURB ME* zone,
In a beehive of activity,
The lazy yawning drone.

The Circus

When it comes into the village,
Dad goes there no more;
Dad took me to the circus
Every year since I was four –

He'd take me to the circus
And he'd sit with me
In the middle of all the children
Until, gradually,

As I got a little older,
I'd go away from Dad
And sit with all my school friends
(I wonder was he sad?);

But, now that I'm eleven,
The circus is a bore;
I don't go to the circus.
Now Dad goes there no more.

The Dreamer

I play with all my classmates
But I've got no special friend –
No-one likes me that much,
They all leave me to fend

For myself when school is out
So I just play alone
Imagining all sorts of things
In our backyard at home.

And Mam and Dad both ask me
Why I don't have friends to play
But I just smile and tell them
It's OK.

'Cos the games that I am playing
Are not like other games
(Games like those we play at school
Bound by rules and names)

And I can play them anywhere
'Cos all I have to do
Is find a quiet space in my mind
And let the dreams come through.

My Boots Are as High as my Mammy's

My boots are as high as my mammy's,
I got them last week in Tralee;
My boots are as high as my mammy's
And Mammy is smiling at me:

She knows that her daughter is growing,
She can see that I'm growing up tall
Though somewhere deep down inside her
I'm her baby, helpless and small.

My boots are as high as my mammy's,
She can see that I'm growing up tall –
Soon she knows I'll no longer
Be Mammy's baby at all,
Yes, soon she knows I'll no longer
Be her little baby at all.

Tickles

When I was young, oh! years ago
(Like when I was four),
My daddy used to tickle me
But I don't have tickles no more
(Not much).

'Cos when you're four, tickles
Are a kind of game,
But when you're ten, you don't feel
Like playing tickles no more
(Not much);

'Cos now I'm ten, I'm bigger
And such games are a bore
(Well kind of)
And when Daddy tries to tickle me
I don't have tickles no more
(Not much).

And Daddy realizes
That I'm a big girl now
And tickles and such are over
And no matter how
We try to play at tickles
Like we used to do before
It's not the same for me or him
'Cos I don't have tickles no more
(Not much)
'Cos I don't have tickles no more.

Bath Time

When you're young, a bath is where
You play with all your toys –
You splash and thrash about in it
Making suds and noise;

You dive below the water
Like a submarine,
Or down there like Old Faithful
You blow up spray and steam;

For when you're young, a bath is where
You play and spray and splash,
But when you're older, all it is
Is a tub in which you wash.
A bath tub.

Don't Squash Fluffy

Fluffy is our Westie
(A West Highland terrier),
When my sister goes to bed at night
He jumps in beside her
And he lies there on the duvet
Snug as snug can be;
When I come in to say goodnight
Sister says to me,
"DON'T SQUASH FLUFFY!"

And when Mammy's sitting
On the sofa late at night
Watching television
By the turf firelight,
Fluff jumps up beside her
There on the settee
And when I come in to say goodnight
Mammy says to me,
"DON'T SQUASH FLUFFY!"

DON'T SQUASH FLUFFY!
Is all I ever get –
No wonder that our Fluffy's
Such a little pet;
DON'T SQUASH FLUFFY!
Or someone will get cross;
DON'T SQUASH FLUFFY!
'Cos Fluffy is the boss
In our house.
Fluffy!

Good Friday

Why's it called "Good Friday"?
I'd have said 'twas bad,
The day that Christ was crucified,
Christ, the Son of God.

Why's it called "Good Friday"?
Daddy says to me
That Good Friday's good because
Christ died to set us free

And by dying on Good Friday
He saved us from our sins.
OK – so it was good for us.
But not so good for him.
Good Friday.

Child Swatting a Wasp

Swatting a wasp with your book is fine
(You'd think there'd be no "buts"
'Cos you're afraid he'll sting you)
Until you see his guts

Splattered on the cover
All bloody, streaky goo –
At first you're glad you killed him,
And then it dawns on you

That you've just killed and will kill again,
You kill the things you fear,
But though you kill and kill and kill
The wasp is always here;

And every wasp that's splattered
All bloody, streaky goo
Just proves that killing's useless.
What scares you most is you.

The Frog

Out of the prickly heather,
Out of the mushy bog,
Over the wobbly fresh-cut turf
Came the frog.

And Mattie Quinn and Dad and John
Stopped briefly from their work
As I ran between the lines
Of wobbly fresh-cut turf.

I tried to catch him but he jumped,
He was a hoppy frog,
But I tried again and caught him.
Would I take him from his bog

And keep him in a jar at home
Where he could be my pet
Far away from the mushy bog
Where life was wobbly wet?

I thought about it while the frog
Sat softly in my hands,
Then released him to his bog.
He hopped off at once

Over the prickly heather,
Over the mushy bog,
Over the wobbly fresh-cut turf.
My frog.

Jacko

Jacko is our cockatiel
And he can imitate
The sound of anything he hears,
And boy! he's accurate.

He whistles at the ladies
Wolf-whistles that he heard
In the pet shop in his cage
As a little bird.

But best of all the things he does
Is when you're out the back,
He rings just like the telephone –
You rush in and find it's Jack;

It's not the telephone at all!;
Brother! You've been had
Once again by Jacko;
It's enough to drive you mad,

But you don't get mad at Jacko
Even though he's a lad.
No! You don't get mad at Jacko
Even though you've just been had.

Oh, Jacko!

Summer's Here!

Summer's here! Summer's here!
A bumble bee is out;
Even though it's still not May,
I see him fly about.

He's flying among the flowers of spring,
The first of summer, he,
For summer's here! Yes, summer's here!
When you see the bumble bee.

He's flying among the flowers of spring
Although it's still not May
'Cos he felt the summer in the air
This take-your-coat-off day.

He's flying among the flowers of spring
Beside the garden shed;
He's woken up the summer
In every hedge and bed.

Summer's here! Yes, summer's here!
A bumble bee is out;
You know that summer's here at last
When you see him fly about,
The bumble bee.